Orion Books Ltd

Orion House

5 Upper St Martin's Lane

London WC2H 9EA

First published by Orion 1997

Drawings by Michael Martin

Cover illustrations by Alex Graham

© Associated Newspapers plc 1997

ISBN 0 75280 908 3

Printed and bound in Great Britain
by The Guernsey Press Limited.

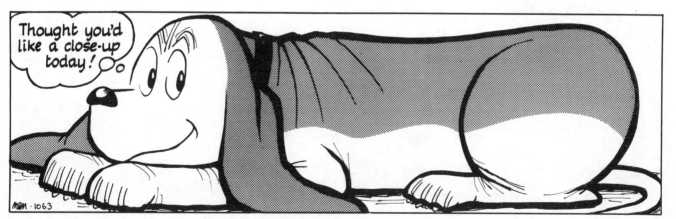

Ever since their trip to the end-of-season sale at the garden centre...

...I get this eerie feeling I'm being constantly watched!

MGM · 1040

Here comes that French poodle from number thirty-three

1041

He's a nice enough chap, but I prefer to keep my distance

...It's the garlic, you know!

MGM

LOOK AT THAT CAT LYING IN THE FLOWER BED

A cat in our garden? Leave this to me!

LOOKS LIKE MRS CHARLTON'S BIG GINGER TOM

Mrs Charlton's big ginger tom?

COME ON, FRED, *GO CHASE HIM OFF!*

...on second thoughts!

MRM · 105B

WHAT'S THE CAPITAL CITY OF AUSTRALIA?

MELBOURNE. AH, NO, SORRY, IT'S CANBERRA

105

WHAT'S THE CHEMICAL FORMULA FOR SODIUM BICARBONATE?

ER, PASS

'Pass'? Don't tell me he's studying for Mastermind!

YOU ONLY PASSED ON TWO   OH GOOD, I THINK WE STAND A GOOD CHANCE OF BEATING *THE RED LION*

Ah, the pub quiz on Friday!

MRM

1060

1061

IT'S SO DIFFICULT, THEY'RE ALL NICE...

Please come along, we've been in this shoe shop for *ages*. I'm bored to tears!

...THE BLUE PAIR I RATHER LIKE... BUT THEN THE RED ONES WOULD GO WITH MY DRESS— *OH, I JUST DON'T KNOW WHAT TO DO...*

...You're not the only one!

1077

You wouldn't think that a mere ginger tom could terrorise a whole neighbourhood, would you?

1078

...but he does!

That wretched cat of Mrs Charlton thinks he can outsmart me!

...He's turned into a dead end, now I'll teach him a lesson

Yipes! - A cats' trap!

1083

I BUMPED INTO THAT DREADFUL WOMAN FROM FARLEY AVENUE TODAY...

OH, YES?

1084

...SHE WAS BOASTING ABOUT THAT PRECIOUS LABRADOR OF HERS — APPARENTLY IT HAS A LONG PEDIGREE AND A FANCY NAME TO MATCH, SO I TOLD HER OUR FRED IS NATIONAL CHAMPION

...AND HIS PEDIGREE NAME IS FREDERICK POMPADOUR BASSETON THE THIRD

A little white lie, but I rather like it!

He's ruining my afternoon nap...

...Snoring his head off like that, I can't possibly sleep...

That was a close thing! I only escaped that wretched Jack Russell by scrambling on to this shed roof!

YAP YAP YAP YAP

1086

...Don't ask me how I did it!

YAP YAP

...and don't ask me how I'm going to get down!

'With the arrival of Venus in your sign, you may feel time is passing very slowly'... Mmm — true...

'You may also feel something essential is missing from your life' —Mmm, **very true**!

1132

...My dinner!

MGM

HOW DID YOU GET ON?

He's got good news and bad news...

1133

I LOST

OH

The bad news...

...BUT I WON THE JACKPOT ON THE CLUBHOUSE FRUIT MACHINE!

NO!

The good news!

We've been to little Amanda's birthday party...

...I've been spoilt rotten. I've eaten toffee apples, cakes, biscuits, sweets and even some jelly. I've had a wonderful time...

...although my stomach is starting to think differently!

1153

Little Amanda got a basset hound for her birthday

Here she is now, taking him out for a walk...

...or should I say, a *push!*

1154

She's coming home from her sister's today but, unfortunately, in his rush to do some last minute dusting...

1165

...he broke her favourite vase!

So now he's doing some last minute gluing!

M&M

FORE!

1166

Hey! Steady on!

SORRY, FRED

Is nowhere safe when he's playing?

M&M

My favourite event is the hundred metre dash!

1167

On your marks... get set...

GO!

We may not have the same tastes...

1168

...but we can still enjoy a little window shopping together!

Ladies FASHION

FAMILY BUTCHER

ATISHOOOO!

EXCUSE ME, VICAR — I DO APOLOGISE

Jolly good timing, I'd say...

1169.

I'M VERY SORRY— IT LOOKS LIKE WE'LL HAVE TO START AGAIN

YES, IT DOES

The vicar was just about to checkmate him!

Her soufflé has risen beautifully. A triumph!

Quick, before it collapses

1170

Too late!

WHAT'S THAT?

*Well, did **I** win, or did **you** blink first?*

1179

OH, I MUST GO AND FEED RUPERT

1180

The Johnsons are away on holiday, so we're looking after Rupert for a while

Silly name for a rubber plant, if you ask me!

PLANT FEED

FRED!

WHAT THE BLAZES ARE YOU TALKING ABOUT! — WHAT A LOAD OF RUBBISH!

Oh dear, what's she gone and done now?

THAT'S A BLATANT LIE IF EVER I HEARD ONE!

She must have been up to something horrendous to put him in such a foul mood...

— OH YEAH — YOU PROMISED THAT LAST TIME!

Oh, my mistake, it's only a party political broadcast!

HERE'S YOUR DINNER

WHAT IS IT TONIGHT, DEAR?

IT'S A SORT OF COTTAGE PIE SPECIAL. I MADE IT UP AS I WENT ALONG, IT'S GOT A FEW LEFT-OVER THINGS IN IT — THE TOPPING'S A LITTLE SLOPPY, BUT I THINK IT SHOULD TASTE OK

HOW NICE

Rather you than me, mate!

The Joneses really spoil that terrier of theirs

It should be a crime giving all those bones to one little dog...

...Share and share alike, that's what I say!

MBM·1234

The church needs a new roof — that's the only reason I'm doing this!

...It's all for a good cause, I keep telling myself — ignore the ridicule

1237

Poor lass, she's got a nasty Summer cold...

...and very miserable she is with it, too; she's taken herself off to bed

1261
MBM

Still, she's gaining some comfort from the Ladies' Finals!

I AM THE EVIL DR. X, AND WHO ARE YOU?

THE NAME IS BOND —JAMES BOND!

1263

AND WHO, MAY I ASK, IS YOUR ACCOMPLICE?

The name is Basset...

MBM

...Fred Basset!

We're off on our little holiday break

1268

NOW, DO YOU THINK THAT'S THE LOT?

I SURE HOPE SO

...but, unlike them...

COME ALONG, FRED

...I'm travelling light!

Just look at that breathtaking view

...miles and miles of rolling countryside

...what an ideal spot to break down!

1269

This man is on a mission — to explore the dark corners of space...

...to seek out what once was lost — to boldly go where no man has gone before...

1276

...The loft!

I'M SURE IT'S UP THERE SOMEWHERE

NOW DO BE CAREFUL UP THERE, WON'T YOU?

CRASH

ARE YOU ALL RIGHT?

1277

BLAST!

He's OK — but the bedroom ceiling isn't!

I'M SORRY, SIR, YOUR CAR HAS FAILED THE M.O.T.!

OH DEAR

GARAGE

AFTER A THOROUGH CHECK, WE'VE FOUND WORN WIPER BLADES, EXCESSIVE MOVEMENT IN THE HANDBRAKE AND THE EXHAUST EMISSION IS TOO HIGH...

OH

PLUS THE NEARSIDE BRAKE LIGHT DOESN'T WORK AND THE OFFSIDE INDICATOR...

That evening class in car maintenance is going to come in handy!

There's something very peaceful about watching the sailing boats gracefully bobbing along on the water

What the blazes? Where did that submarine come from?

...I might have known— the Tucker twins!